Just Like Daddy

FRANK ASCH

HOUGHTON MIFFLIN COMPANY

BOSTON

ATLANTA   DALLAS   GENEVA, ILLINOIS   PALO ALTO   PRINCETON

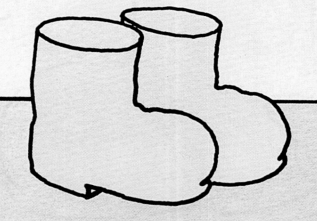

To Devin

When I got up this morning
I yawned a big yawn...

Just like Daddy.

I washed my face, got dressed,
and had a big breakfast...

Just like Daddy.

Then I put on my coat
and my boots...

Just like Daddy.

And we all went fishing.

On the way I picked a flower
and gave it to my mother...

Just like Daddy.

When we got to the lake,
I put a big worm on my hook...

Just like Daddy.

All day we fished and fished,
and I caught a big fish...

Just like Mommy!

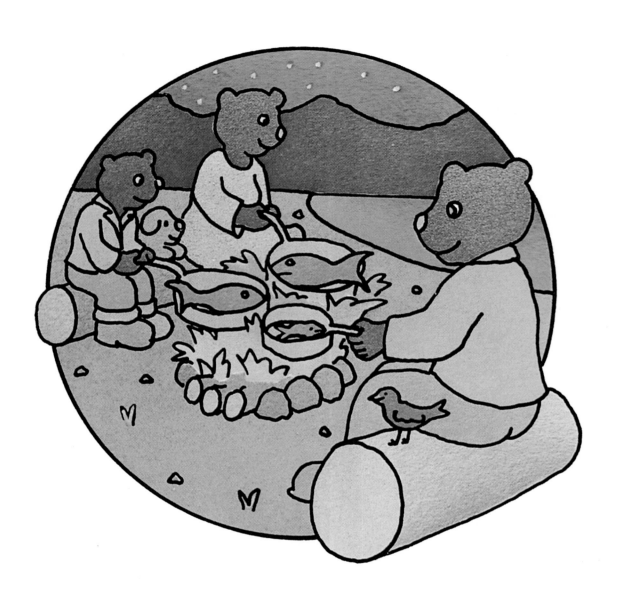